CLASSIC LANDFORMS OF THE

WHITE PEAK

CLASSIC LANDFORMS OF THE

WHITE PEAK

ROGER DALTON, HOWARD FOX AND PETER JONES
University of Derby

Series editors
Rodney Castleden and Christopher Green

Published by the Geographical Association
in conjunction with the
British Geomorphological Research Group

THE GEOGRAPHICAL ASSOCIATION

THE BRITISH GEOMORPHOLOGICAL RESEARCH GROUP

PREFACE

Geomorphologists study landforms and the processes that create and modify them. The results of their work, published as they invariably are in specialist journals, usually remain inaccessible to the general public. We would like to put that right. Scattered across the landscapes of England and Wales there are many beautiful and striking landforms that delight the eye of the general public and are also visited by educational parties from schools, colleges and universities. Our aim in producing this series of guides is to make modern explanations of these classic landforms available to all, in a style and format that will be easy to use in the field. We hope that an informed understanding of the origins of the features will help the visitor to enjoy the landscape all the more.

Encouraged by the success of the first edition of the Classic Landform Guides we are pleased to introduce this new edition, enhanced by colour photographs, new illustrations and with the valuable addition of 1:50 000 map extracts by kind permission of the Education Team, Ordnance Survey. The relevant maps for the area covered in this booklet are: Ordnance Survey Maps 1:63 360 Peak District Tourist Map; the 1:50 000 Landranger sheets 110, 118 and 119 and the Ordnance Survey 1:25 000 Outdoor Leisure Maps No 1 (The Dark Peak) and No 24 (The White Peak). Please refer to the current Ordnance Survey Index for the availability of other 1:25 000 sheets.

Rodney Castleden *Roedean School, Brighton*
Christopher Green *Royal Holloway, University of London*

CONTENTS

Cover photograph: Lathkill Dale. Photo: Roger Dalton.
Frontispiece: Manifold Valley: Thor's Cave. Photo: Roger Dalton.
Acknowledgements
The Geographical Association would like to thank the following organisation for
permission to reproduce material in this publication:
Mapping reproduced from Ordnance Survey 1:50 000 Landranger mapping
with the permission of The Controller of Her Majesty's Stationery Office
© Crown Copyright 82324M 09/96
Illustrations: Paul Coles
Series design concept: Quarto Design, Huddersfield
Design and typesetting: ATG Design Communication, Huddersfield
Printed and bound in Hong Kong by: Colorcraft Limited

INTRODUCTION

The Peak District comprises the southernmost part of the Pennines and is essentially an upland dominated by plateau-like surfaces which are dissected by river valleys. It is an extensive yet compact tract of territory extending some 30km from west to east and 50km from north to south giving an area approaching 1600km². The core of the southern and central part of the Peak, occupying over one-quarter of the total area, is made up of Dinantian (Carboniferous) limestone which gives rise to a distinctive range of landforms. This is the area popularly known as 'the White Peak' as a result of the distinctive pale grey coloration of limestone outcrops, quarry faces and walls especially when illuminated by sunlight. It contrasts with 'the Dark' or 'High Peak' coincident with the generally more elevated outcrops of Namurian (Carboniferous) gritstones, sandstones and shales which occur to the west, north and east (Figure 1).

It is important that something of the complex geology of both the Dinantian and Namurian (the lower and the middle major divisions of the Carboniferous period, respectively) is appreciated. In the seas of the Lower Carboniferous, limestones were laid down in three distinct environments. The central area of the present limestone outcrop comprised a large shallow-water **carbonate platform.** Around its margins lay a belt of 'reefs' (carbonate mounds) while beyond, there were deeper water basins in which successions of impure limestones and shales were deposited. Apart from variations in rock type which can be related to these contrasting depositional environments, further complexity arises because some of the limestones have undergone secondary alteration to **dolomite.** The occurrence of interbedded volcanic rocks and igneous intrusions plus widespread mineralisation adds yet more diversity, notably, but not exclusively, to the eastern half of the Dinantian limestone outcrop. The succeeding Namurian strata also exhibit significant variations which arise from rhythmic changes in environmental conditions at the time of deposition. The lowest members of the Namurian comprise a thick succession of shales (the Edale Shales) but these pass upwards into alternating shales and sandstones. It is the coarser varieties of sandstone which give rise to the popular term Millstone Grit.

In terms of geological structure the Peak District is commonly described as a dome and is represented as a broad anticlinal feature in west to east cross-sections (Figure 1b). However, the detailed structure is complex with the Carboniferous rocks having been deformed around various fold axes. Deformation occurred on more than one occasion and some of the early structures were modified

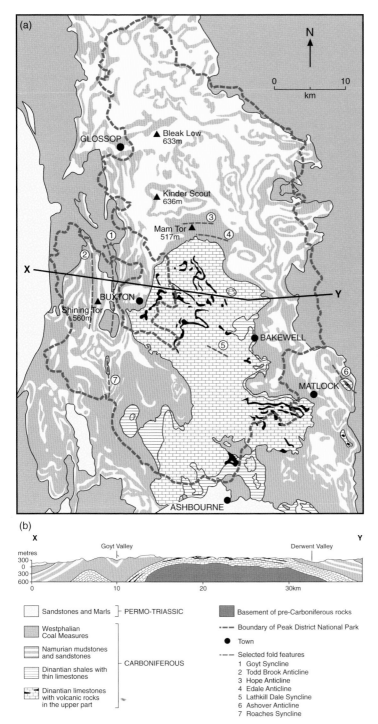

Figure 1: Peak District *(a) simplified geology, and (b) geological cross-section.*

during subsequent folding episodes. Of particular geomorphological interest are some of the minor fold structures which occur at the margins of the Peak District. For example, The Roaches and Goyt Valley **Synclines** to the west and the Crich and Ashover **Anticlines** to the east all have a structural expression in the landscape, the latter bringing the Dinantian to the surface (Dalton *et al.*, 1999). Faulting has also affected the Carboniferous rocks but is of little geomorphological significance except on a local scale.

The major elements of the relief and drainage of the Peak District may be briefly summarised thus:

1. The plateau-like surfaces characteristic of the White Peak and the Dark Peak increase in elevation in a northerly direction from

Table 1: Major stages in the development of the
Peak District landscape

Stage *climate*	Approximate date (years BP)	Geomorphological activity
Holocene (postglacial) *Temperate*		Re-establishment of interglacial stream pattern; lowering of water tables to produce tributary valleys; formation of modern floodplains, development of soil and vegetation cover, variously stabilisation of slopes and reactivation of landslips; formation of peat and flowstone; further desiccation of limestone valleys through construction of mine drains; increasing modification of natural landscape due to human activities.
Late Pleistocene Devensian (last glacial) *Cold (with short warm phases)*	10,000	Periglacial degradation, freeze-thaw weathering, scree formation, tor formation, landslips, solifluction, deposition of sheets of head; smoothing out of irregularities, levelling of interfluves; valley incision by seasonal streams
Ipswichian (last interglacial) *Temperate*	110,000	Dissection of glacial deposits on interfluves, fluvial aggradation in main valleys, deep weathering of bedrock; precipitation of tufa and **speleothems.**
Middle Pleistocene *Alternations of cold and temperate episodes*	130,000	During cold stages: glacial erosion of bedrock and older drift deposits; deposition of till over an irregular land surface; widespread drainage modification initiating present-day drainage pattern. During temperate stage: formation of deeply weathered regoliths; expansion of cave systems by sub-surface flow.
Early Pleistocene *General cooling but with climatic fluctuations*	700,000	Continued uplift; erosion of pre-Pleistocene landscape; valley incision; cave formation in limestone areas; subsidence of Neogene sediments caused by limestone solution.
Late Tertiary or Neogene	1,800,000 25,000,000	Emergence of upland Britain and initiation of streams; exposure of Carboniferous bedrock; deposition of sediments (Brassington Formation) over a former land surface some 150m above present ground level; progressive uplift of Peak District.

Photo 1: Wolfescote Dale: *A typical valley cross-profile incorporating free face and scree. Photo: Roger Dalton.*

Photo 2: Limestone plateau: *soil profile of loess intermixed with solution debris. Photo: Peter Jones.*

approximately 270m OD in the vicinity of Wirksworth, to about 650m OD on the Kinder Scout Plateau west of Sheffield.

2. Except on the northern margins, the pattern of drainage is dominated by southward-draining tributaries of the River Trent.

3. The Derwent River system is of greatest significance. It drains much of the northern, central and eastern parts of the Peak, whilst the Dove/Manifold system drains the western margin (Photo 1 and frontispiece).

9

Much of the detail of the present relief can be related to the effects of climatic change on the operation of erosional and depositional systems during recent geological time (Table 1). Knowledge of past conditions is inevitably less certain the further one goes back in time

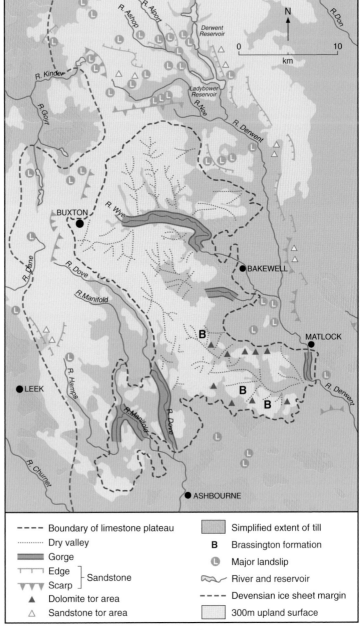

Figure 2: Major landform features of the Peak District.

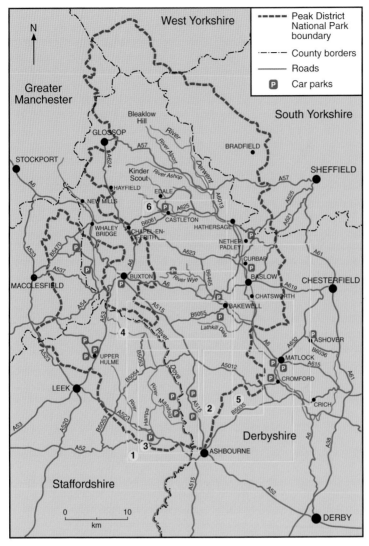

Figure 3: The Peak District: location, access and areas covered by this guide.

but key aspects are the extent and severity of glacial episodes. The impact of such events on the limestone landscapes of the White Peak is noteworthy in a number of respects.

The area was over-ridden by ice on at least two occasions in the Middle Pleistocene (Table 1). The **till** deposits from these episodes are limited but clearly indicate ice movement from the north. During the Devensian glaciation the White Peak lay close to, yet beyond, the ice margins (Figure 2). It is apparent that unvegetated rock surfaces were subject to deflation and windblown particles or **loess** were deposited across the plateau of the White Peak. Modern soils may have up to 0.5m of loessic material incorporated into them (Photo 2). The combination of the above factors may help to explain the absence from the White Peak of limestone pavements found in West Yorkshire. **Periglacial** phenomena occur widely, notably **tors** and screes, but very much as modifications to a fluvially-fashioned landscape. Indeed, Sweeting (1972) has described the White Peak as a classic area of fluvial karst substantially dependent on **allogenic** drainage (i.e. rivers originating on the impermeable strata at the margins of the limestone which may in total or in part sustain their courses across the limestone). For all these rivers, for example the Dove and the Wye, the great majority of tributary valleys are dry, suggesting a progressive lowering of the water table and extensive development of subterranean drainage systems. To date some 40km of underground channels and caves have been explored.

Whilst the landforms referred to in this volume need to be seen in the context of the geological and geomorphological circumstances summarised above, the human impact on the landscape must not be overlooked. In particular the effects of agricultural practices since prehistoric times (mainly deforestation) together with the consequences of mining, quarrying and tourism must be borne in mind.

As it is impossible to refer to all the localities of potential interest within the White Peak, what is offered here is a selective but representative coverage. The major features of the physical landscape of the White Peak are summarised in Figure 2, and location and access is indicated in Figure 3.

THE LIMESTONE PLATEAU

Photo 3: Limestone plateau near Chelmorton. Photo: Roger Dalton.

The plateau surface

The limestone outcrop of the White Peak (Figure 1) gives rise to a distinctive upland of gently rolling hills and deeply incised dales. Throughout much of this area the ground surface rises to between 300 and 370m OD and takes on the appearance of a dissected plateau. The largest single tract of unbroken plateau is on the Dove/Wye interfluve south-east of Buxton. This is followed, in part, by the A515 between Buxton and Ashbourne from which there are extensive views over a seemingly monotonous windswept landscape. Elsewhere the continuity of the plateau is disrupted by the deep incisions of the major streams and by the shallower but more intricate networks of **dry valleys** (Figure 2). Despite this fragmentation, there is a general uniformity of surface heights over a wide area of the limestone outcrop and skyline profiles are horizontal (Photo 3).

Although a casual observer might easily be deceived by the apparent simplicity of the plateau surface, the more perceptive visitor soon discovers a wide range of geomorphological features. Prominent limestone mounds and ridges, dolomite tors, solution phenomena, silica sand pockets together with a patchy cover of superficial deposits all contribute to significant scenic variety. In addition, the deep valleys and limestone gorges, some with rugged crags, scree-clad slopes, striking rock pinnacles and buttresses, **sink** holes (or

swallets) and caves create even greater diversity. Some morphological irregularities in the present-day landscape reflect variations in the bedrock geology. However, there is a lack of any consistent relationship between the plateau surface and the sometimes complex structure displayed by the limestones. In places the plateau has been bevelled across major folds in the bedrock and has a markedly discordant form.

Taken as a whole the limestone plateau is the most significant element of the landscape of the White Peak. Its regional development, sub-horizontal form and lack of concordance with the geological structure gives it the appearance of an uplifted **planation surface**. Often referred to as the 'Peak District Upland Surface', its origin has been the subject of much debate. Opinion has differed over the age of the feature and the degree to which it was subsequently modified. The problem remains unresolved, although it is clear that any explanation of the present morphology of the limestone plateau must take into account aspects of the Carboniferous and post-Carboniferous geology of the area as well as the sequence of geomorphological events which occurred during late Tertiary and Quaternary times.

The geological history of the Peak District limestones is complex (see Ford, 1977 for a comprehensive review). The following aspects are emphasised here because of their particular geomorphological significance:

1. The present limestone upland represents the approximate extent of the marine carbonate platform which existed during the Lower Carboniferous and on which well-bedded and relatively pure shallow-water limestones were deposited. Shales and thinly bedded impure limestones that originally formed in deeper water basins around the margins of the platform have proved to be more susceptible to modern erosion. In general they have been cut down

Photo 4: The scarp-like edge of the carbonate platform near Dove Dale viewed *from the south. Photo: Roger Dalton.*

to create a marked topographic discontinuity around the edge of the plateau, thus accentuating its relief (Photo 4). Contrasting with the well-bedded rocks are irregular mounds of unstratified limestones (reefs) which formed on the shallow-water platform as carbonate banks. These are variously developed throughout the area, but are particularly common at the platform margins (Figure 2, page 10). The mounds frequently form conspicuous features and are well preserved in the landscape around Castleton, Matlock and Dove Dale.

2. Toadstones (basaltic lavas, **tuffs** and associated igneous intrusions) found within the limestone sequence are significant in several ways. Unlike the limestones they act as impermeable barriers to groundwater flow, thus influencing the pattern of underground drainage and the development of caves. Already strongly decomposed as a result of chemical alteration, the toadstones usually weather easily and tend to form surface depressions rather than positive landscape features. On some valley sides, in situations where the rocks are steeply inclined, **slip planes** have developed along the water-lubricated and softened tops of toadstone layers. An impressive example of a former rock slide is the detached Peter's Stone crag in Cressbrook Dale (SK 174753) which has moved on the surface of a tuff horizon.

3. The carbonate platform was subjected to contemporaneous uplift and erosion prior to the deposition of the Namurian shales. This resulted in an uneven limestone surface which is currently being **exhumed** through differential erosion of the shales. Spectacular topographic irregularities in the sub-Namurian surface are exemplified by the knobbly form of the plateau margin at Earl Sterndale where the limestone **inliers** of Chrome Hill (SK 071674) and Parkhouse Hill (SK 080669) rise prominently above the surrounding shales. A contrasting feature is the Winnats Pass at Castleton which is thought to represent an exhumed sub-marine channel.

4. Prolonged erosion during Permo-Triassic times removed a substantial thickness of Upper Carboniferous sediments from above the former limestone platform and even exposed the limestone in some areas. This was certainly the case in the extreme south-west where Permo-Triassic rocks now lie in direct contact with the Dinantian limestones of the Weaver Hills (SK 095464). The widespread dolomitisation of the southern part of the limestone outcrop is thought to have occurred during the same period due to the infiltration of layers near the surface by magnesium-rich solutions. Whatever its origin, the dolomitisation has important geomorphological implications. The more porous areas of dolomitised limestone acted as preferential routes in groundwater movement and have been affected by differential

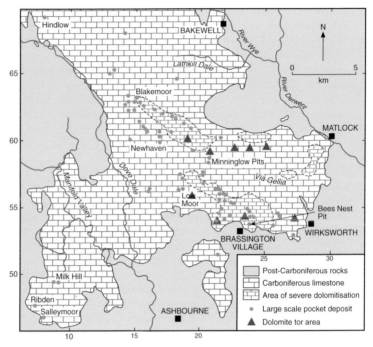

Figure 4: The southern limestone outcrop showing dolomitised areas and the location of dolomite tors and pocket deposits.

solution and collapse. There is also a close relationship between the severely dolomitised zone and the distribution of limestone tors (Figure 4).

5. Following a period of marine submergence during the late Mesozoic, there was uplift and further erosion in the Tertiary. The remaining cover of Permo-Triassic and Upper Carboniferous sediments was progressively removed resulting in eventual exposure of the limestone. Some of the limestone outcrop was undoubtedly further revealed during the Quaternary, but the extent and degree of Quaternary erosion is difficult to assess. The ice sheets which overrode the Peak District in the pre-Devensian glacial episodes certainly moulded the surface to some degree because material from the limestone outcrop has been recognised in the till sheets of the Midlands to the south. Glacial till deposits on the limestone plateau are limited in extent. A good example is located in the vicinity of Shining Bank Quarry (SK 229652) (Photos 5a and b). The footpath which runs to the north of the quarry enables viewing of the exposed till at the top of the quarry face. This till has been shown to be up to 12m in thickness and to incorporate limestone boulders and debris, sandstone from the Namurian and material from the Borrowdale volcanics of the Lake District.

Photo 5: Shining Bank Quarry:
*(a) 12m of till is visible above the quarry face, and (b) detail of till: limestone **clasts** in clay matrix. Photo: Peter Jones.*

When the origin of the limestone plateau is considered against this geological background the reasons for uncertainty over its age become clear. The limestones were accessible to erosion during the mid-Carboniferous, Permo-Triassic, Tertiary and Quaternary periods, and in any or all of these, truncation of the geological structure could have occurred. However, two lines of evidence suggest that the present planar form of the plateau surface is of recent date.

First, tentative reconstructions of the sub-Namurian and sub-Triassic surfaces indicate that both have uneven relief. Second, Tertiary sediments preserved in deep pockets on the southern part of the limestone outcrop around Brassington Village imply that the present plateau level is already some distance below a former Tertiary (or sub-Neogene) land surface (Figure 5a, page 19).

TERTIARY SEDIMENTS: THE BRASSINGTON FORMATION

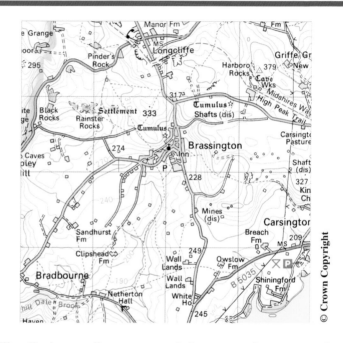

© Crown Copyright

The Tertiary sediments owe their preservation to massive subsidence following sub-surface solution and localised collapse of the limestones and still tend to correlate with depressions in the plateau surface. They comprise gravels, sands and clays often highly disturbed by downwarping calculated to be between 150 and 250m in some cases. Some of the uppermost clays contain distinctive plant remains of late Tertiary (Neogene) age. The underlying sediments are considered to be largely of fluvial origin, and probably once formed a continuous cover over the southern part of the Peak District. Such a cover was subsequently removed by erosion (Figure 5a) and only the isolated pockets remain today (Figure 5b). Collectively, these sediments are referred to as the Brassington Formation.

More than 60 pocket deposits are known from the area south of Bakewell, and others may lie undetected. They have been extensively worked as a source of refractory sand and several sections are currently accessible. One of the most instructive is the Bees Nest Pit 1km north-east of Brassington village (Figure 6) (Photo 6). The inclined entrance road to the Bees Nest Pit (SK 240546) cuts through an unconformable capping of Pleistocene glacial deposits which can

18

(a)

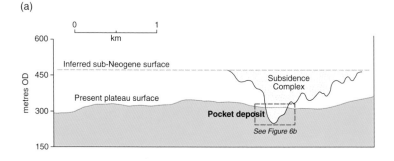

(b)

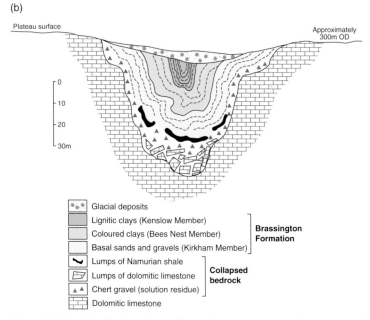

	Glacial deposits	
	Lignitic clays (Kenslow Member)	**Brassington Formation**
	Coloured clays (Bees Nest Member)	
	Basal sands and gravels (Kirkham Member)	
	Lumps of Namurian shale	**Collapsed bedrock**
	Lumps of dolomitic limestone	
	Chert gravel (solution residue)	
	Dolomitic limestone	

Figure 5: Pocket deposits (Brassington Formation) (a) in relation to the evolution of the limestone plateau surface, and (b) a cross-section through a typical pocket deposit.

also be seen around the upper margins of the excavation (Figure 6). The floor of the pit exposes basal sands and gravels (Kirkham Member), some of which are strongly cemented. Overlying these, on the northern side near to the entrance, are unfossiliferous coloured clays (Bees Nest Member) in which steeply dipping bedding is clearly discernible. On a higher level, 20m east of the entrance road, is a small patch of organic or lignite clay (Kenslow Member) containing numerous wood fragments of late Tertiary age. At several places around the western edge of the excavation dolomite wall-rocks may be seen, both *in situ* and as detached blocks. In direct contact with this is a Chert-clay gravel up to 5m thick which is considered to be a solution residue from the limestone. Also present around the margins and below the Tertiary sediments are disturbed masses of black

Photo 6: The Bee's Nest Pit. *Photo: Peter Jones.*

Namurian shale, sometimes weathered to a lilac colour. These suggest that the Brassington Formation was deposited (at least locally) on a veneer of shales rather than directly on the limestone surface itself.

Estimates of the thicknesses of limestone and Namurian shale existing at this and other sites prior to solutional collapse indicate that the land surface on which the Brassington Formation was deposited lay at about 450m relative to modern sea-level. This is approximately 150m above the present plateau surface (Figure 5a). As the deposits are thought to have formed on a low-lying floodplain close to sea-level approximately 6 million years **BP**, it is evident that there has since been substantial uplift as well as widespread surface lowering. A major cause of the surface lowering is likely to have been differential solution of the limestone. A theoretical model proposed by Pitty (1968) demonstrates how steady solution action on a progressively unroofed limestone dome could produce a central plateau surface. Making allowances for irregularities in the limestone/shale contact, it can be argued that recent solutional lowering and not earlier **peneplanation** has been responsible for the bevelled form of the plateau. If this view is correct, the modern limestone plateau represents not a well preserved uplifted relict from the past but:

'... a continually developing erosion surface at one brief instant in its evolution' (Pitty, 1968, p. 174).

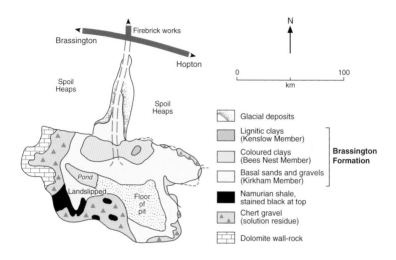

Figure 6: The Bee's Nest Pit.

Dolomite tors

The limestone of the south-eastern part of the plateau has been altered locally to dolomite (Figures 2 and 4). Where it outcrops the dolomite is porous and weathers more easily than unaltered limestone. As a result prominent crags and upstanding masses of bare rock known as tors are a conspicuous feature of the dolomite landscape but do not exist on the unaltered limestone. All the dolomite tors occur at heights between 250 and 350m OD. They vary in character from isolated stacks and pinnacles only 15m high such as Grey Tor (SK 234604) and Wyns Tor (SK 243601), near Winster Village, to castellated escarpments 60m or more in height and 1km in length such as at Rainster Rocks (Figure 7) north-west of Brassington village. This latter location provides a good example of the dolomite tor landscape. At Rainster Rocks (SK 218548) a **free face** scarp overlooks a broad dry valley to the south and is terminated in its lower western end by the north-south trending Black Rocks ridge (SK 215550). The crest of the scarp forms a narrow spine of bedrock some 15m wide comprising a series of tor masses. These consist of large, generally angular blocks separated by enlarged joints in some places forming pillars of dolomite bedrock. The blocks show only slight rounding of the edges but frequently the faces of the blocks are pitted and cockled by the solutional weathering of calcareous fossils. Detached blocks form a debris slope of about 40° at the foot of the escarpment and the process of detachment by the wedging action of

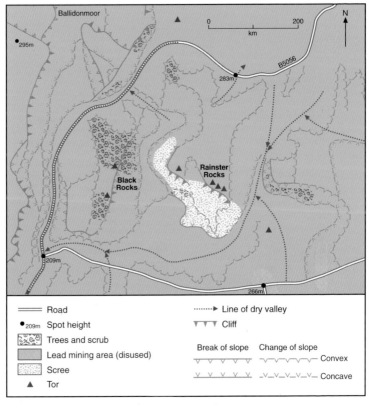

Figure 7: Geomorphological features at Black Rocks and Rainster Rocks.

tree roots may be clearly seen today. Temporary excavations of such debris slopes associated with quarrying have revealed that decalcification of the blocks occurs beneath a soil and vegetation cover. This gives rise to large quantities of incoherent dolomite crystals known as dolomite sand which fills joints and may ultimately completely bury blocks. Indeed at Hopton Top (SK 259547) nearly a complete tor was partially exhumed from its own breakdown products by quarrying. Similar exposure of tor features has occurred during the quarrying of Tertiary silica sand pockets described above (pages 18-19). The walls of some of the depressions have been deeply weathered along joints and complete removal of the silica sand infill would produce a 'wall-tor' form.

Tors as landforms have been the subject of much debate in geomorphology for many years and two main hypotheses of formation have been proposed. The first envisages a period of deep chemical weathering of the bedrock, possibly during warmer climates of the Tertiary. An irregular contact between the weathered mantle and fresh rock is produced by variations in the depth of weathering as determined by the degree of jointing or rock susceptibility to processes of decomposition. Subsequently the weathered mantle is removed by running water or **mass movements** leaving relatively unweathered rock as upstanding tors. A second hypothesis sees tors in Britain as merely one of a group of features produced under cold climate conditions. It is thought that tors are isolated by severe freeze-thaw activity from retreating scarp edges, with **solifluctional** mass movement removing the shattered debris (Dalton *et al.*, 1999).

In the case of the dolomite tors, evidence for both origins can be found. The silica sand deposits indicate the existence of tropical deep weathering conditions during the Tertiary. Such conditions may have produced the enlarged joints of wall-tors in the sand depressions. The tors may then have been exhumed by fluvial activity in the Tertiary or by cold climate removal of weathering debris during the Quaternary. However, it is unlikely that upstanding tors would have survived glacial incursions into the area. Indeed tor blocks have been described in till deposits overlying the silica sands. Since glacier ice was not present in the area during the last glacial period, the Devensian, it is possible that the present-day tors pre-date the last interglacial. On the other hand some deep weathering may have occurred during warm Ipswichian interglacial conditions. Tor exhumation or creation by free face retreat may then have been renewed during the extreme cryogenic activity of the Devensian cold phase. The fallen blocks at the foot of some tors and the 'dolomite sand' in joints suggest that the process of tor formation is at least partly active today.

Access

The limestone plateau is well served by roads, trackways and footpaths and there are numerous car parks and picnic sites. Bridle paths such as the Monsal Trail, Tissington Trail, Manifold Valley Trail and High Peak Trail, constructed along former railway lines, also provide good access. Information on routes such as these, together with details of associated cycle hire schemes and other facilities, can be obtained from the Peak Park Information Centre, Bakewell (Tel: 01629 813227), Peak Park Trail Warden (Tel: 01335 310829) and for cycle hire at Ashbourne (SK 176469; Tel: 01335 343156) and at Parsley Hay (SK 147637; Tel: 01298 84493).

The A5012 between Cromford (SK 295569) and Newhaven (SK 166603) offers easy access to a variety of limestone scenery. Within a distance of 15km, the A5012 climbs steadily from the valley floor of the River Derwent to the summit of the plateau, having initially followed the base of a deep limestone gorge (Griffe Grange Valley, also called Via Gellia). Above Grange Mill (SK 244576) numerous dry valley systems and solutional phenomena are evident – to which access is possible via side roads and on foot. An alternative way of travelling to Newhaven from Cromford is on foot or by bicycle along the High Peak Trail (car parking available at Black Rock, SK 291557).

Rainster Rocks and Black Rocks can be reached on foot from the B5056.

LIMESTONE VALLEYS AND ASSOCIATED FEATURES

Limestone dales

The limestone plateau of the White Peak is dissected by numerous valleys or dales which are a special feature of the area (Figure 2). Some are so deeply incised that they take the form of spectacular gorges: Dove Dale is a magnificent example. The depth of these valleys, together with their complex multi-faceted cross-profiles, has been attributed to relatively rapid but intermittent uplift of the plateau since the formation of the 'Upland (300m) Surface'. However, Pitty's (1968) model of solutional lowering implies that bevelling of the interfluves took place during or after incision of the valleys.

At the present time most of the valleys are dry and have been described by Gunn as 'the most complex dry valley network in Britain' (Gunn, 1985, p. 278). Nevertheless, their form and pattern leave little doubt that they originated as water-cut features. Those that do contain permanent or intermittent streams are fed, with a few exceptions, by sources outside the limestone outcrop. Such streams usually show a marked reduction in discharge as they cross the limestone. Particularly notable is the River Manifold which exhibits spectacular variations in flow depending on the prevailing groundwater levels. Under present circumstances the rivers are clearly misfits since they appear to lack the capacity for valley excavation. Together with the dry tributary valleys they provide evidence of a significant change in hydrological conditions.

Several theories have been advanced to explain the origin of dry valleys (Goudie, 1990). In the case of the Peak District, attention has been drawn to the fact that dry valley patterns on the limestone are remarkably similar to the drainage patterns created by permanent streams on the surrounding Namurian outcrops. Thus it can be argued that the dry valley network was initiated on a former cover of impermeable rocks (e.g. Namurian shales) and was **superimposed** on to the limestone. Subsequent downcutting by the main streams would have led to a gradual lowering of the regional water table and the progressive desiccation of tributary valleys. Valley incision may well have been intermittent due to fluctuations in base level associated with late-Pleistocene glacial and interglacial episodes. However, the effects of climatically-controlled changes in the position of water tables must also be borne in mind. In some areas, the natural level of the water table has been lowered as a result of artificial drainage tunnels or 'soughs' constructed during the eighteenth and nineteenth centuries to drain lead mines. Many of these now guide underground water to the River Derwent which serves as the local base level. A number of rivers such as the Lathkill and Manifold are intermittent, dependent on seasonal rainfall variation.

It is difficult to assess the extent to which the valleys were modified by Pleistocene periglacial processes. Screes cloak many valley sides, but the thick infills of **head** which characterise valleys in adjacent gritstone areas appear to be largely absent. Being resistant to granular disintegration, the limestones may not have yielded suitable solifluctional debris in the same way as porous sandstones and friable shales. Perhaps a major role of the valleys was to channel seasonal meltwater from the plateau surface when the limestone bedrock was rendered impermeable by **permafrost.** During such periods, some solution and incision of the valley floors undoubtedly occurred.

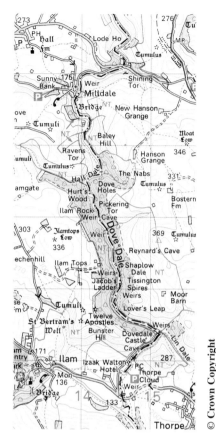

© Crown Copyright

Photo 7: Looking north into Dove Dale from Thorpe Cloud. Photo: Peter Jones.

Incised meanders and associated dry valleys

The Rivers Dove and Manifold cross the south-western extremity of the limestone outcrop in valleys incised up to 200m below the plateau surface (Figure 8). The overall form is best appreciated from high-level vantage points such as Thorpe Cloud (SK 152510, Photo 7) and Thor's Cave (SK 099549, frontispiece). One notable feature is that these valleys exhibit strongly developed meanders which must be distinguished from the meanders of the rivers which occupy them.

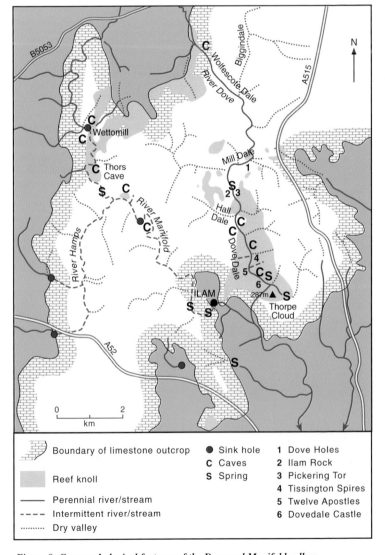

Figure 8: Geomorphological features of the Dove and Manifold valleys.

The latter, though guided by the sinuosity of the valleys, relate to the narrow and discontinuous floodplain tracts on the valley floors. Valley sinuosity is best explained in terms of the erosional history of the limestone plateau as it is likely that contemporary morphology directly relates to the meanders of an early phase in the evolution of the Dove and Manifold valleys. The valley meanders would therefore be produced by downcutting, seemingly over an extended period. However, two complications need to be taken into account:

1. On occasions when the Peak District was overrun by ice from the north or north-west the Dove and Manifold valleys, aligned as they are, may have guided local ice movement and channelled meltwaters during deglaciation. In this event it is questionable whether the initial morphology of the valleys would have survived unmodified.

2. Prominent outcrops of reef limestone exist which partially preserve the morphology of the original carbonate mounds. Between Milldale (SK 140548) and Thorpe Cloud the southward course of the Dove coincides with a large complex of reef limestone. It could be that the restricted development of valley meanders in this locality is a consequence of confinement between carbonate mounds. Similarly in the Manifold Valley, small occurrences of reef limestone at Beeston Tor (SK 106541) and Thor's Cave (SK 099549) have checked the swing of the valley meanders. The meanders of the Manifold Valley have an amplitude up to 800m and a wavelength of up to 600m and are larger than those of the Dove Valley. This may reflect greater discharge from a more extensive catchment and the presence of basinal limestones which incorporate shale bands. In cross-profile the valley meanders exhibit steep cliffs matched by slip-off slopes showing that the stream which fashioned them moved laterally during its incision.

The Rivers Dove and Manifold rise on impermeable Namurian rocks which lie north and west of the Dinantian outcrop (Figure 1) and this enables their flow to be sustained across the limestone. However, the present rivers do not appear large enough to have cut the valleys through which they flow. In common with many rivers in Britain they have a misfit or 'underfit' character. This may be regarded as evidence of overall diminution of discharge, which is also supported by the presence of numerous dry valley tributaries. Both the main valleys and the lower sections of their tributaries are incised but their upper parts, the dry valleys, open out as shallow depressions in the limestone plateau. Moreover, the long profiles of dry tributaries are frequently steep in the lower incised section. In instances such as Hall Dale (SK 140535) and Milldale (SK 139548) there is a noticeable 'hang' above the main valley. This height difference implies more rapid incision by the main stream and supports the progressive desiccation theory of dry valley formation. However, as with many dry valleys a multiprocess origin is probable.

Associated with dry valleys on the Dinantian limestone are other karstic features. The basinal limestones which are dominant in the Dove/Manifold area incorporate shale beds, and cave systems are not extensively developed. Caves occur in association with reef limestones. In Dove Dale, for instance, Thor's Cave (SK 099549), an ancient **phreatic** tube; Dove Holes (SK 142535), possibly fashioned by lateral stream erosion; and Reynard's Cave (SK 145525), with its spectacular arch feature, can all be explored. Swallow holes and spring emergences are also important features of the area. The River Manifold and a number of its tributaries, including the River Hamps, lose flow on entering the limestone outcrop and disappear underground in dry weather. Sinks occur below Wettonmill (SK 096561) on the Manifold, and the river re-emerges at a series of springs near Ilam Hall (SK 132506). By contrast the flow of the River Dove is sustained by weir construction and the lining of its bed with clay to assist fisheries. Springs are evident at the junction of Biggin Dale and Wolfescote Dale (SK 142570) and in variable locations along Lin Dale (SK 153512). Minor seepages on rock faces are common in wet weather and are frequently noticeable as icings during winter frost.

Valley-side features

The extended period of periglacial conditions during the Devensian glaciation resulted in accumulations of blocky debris below free faces of exposed limestone rock. Such screes normally have an angle of rest of about 35° and may be partially covered in vegetation. Occasionally, as at Ecton (SK 096584) in the Manifold Valley, screes have been cemented as a consequence of precipitation of calcium carbonate from percolating lime-rich waters. Many screes occur in Dove Dale, a particularly rewarding series being located on the north-west side of Thorpe Cloud (SK 152510, Photo 8). These appear to result from limestone debris being channelled down gullies or chutes cut into the hill slope. Under present conditions debris accumulation appears to be reduced. The angular nature of the rock fragments suggests that frost action may have been a dominant process. Moreover the outcrops of limestone near the summit of Thorpe Cloud, the logical source of material, are limited in extent and the rate of bedrock disintegration is insufficient to produce large numbers of clasts. The upper parts of the screes are vegetated but the middle and lower parts are largely devoid of vegetation. The upper layer of these exposed areas of scree is unstable, the downslope mobility of clasts being evident from the spill across the Dove-side footpath and into the river itself. The mobile upper layer contrasts with lower layers which comprise smaller clasts with **interstitial** fill. The vegetated margins of the exposed scree are fluctuating and retreat of vegetation may be triggered by seepage of groundwater following wet weather or the effects of trampling by sheep or humans. The gullies containing the

Photo 8: A partially vegetated stone stream *(scree) occupying a former reef channel in Dove Dale. Photo: Peter Jones.*

Photo 9: The 'Twelve Apostles' rock pillars, Dove Dale. *Photo: Peter Jones.*

screes might have originated through the effects of meltwater from snowpatches on the upper slopes of Thorpe Cloud at times of periglacial climate. However it is also possible that gullies may relate to inter-reef or reef-face channels which were formed during the Carboniferous and have subsequently been exhumed.

The particular lithological character of the reefs may also be expressed in the series of spectacular limestone pillars located between Milldale and Lin Dale (Photo 9). As landforms these pillars proved so eye-catching to eighteenth century landscape enthusiasts that they were given romantic names such as Dove Dale Castle, Twelve Apostles and Jacob's Ladder. There is no obvious explanation for these notable features. They have become isolated as the valley sides evolved and indicate resistance to erosion.

Access

The Dove/Manifold area lies within a triangle of major roads A52/A523, A515 and B5053. In this area minor roads are often narrow with occasional severe gradients and sharp bends and so are not suitable for large coaches. Car parks are located at the northern end of Dove Dale on the A515 north of Ashbourne (SK 156549) and at the mouth of Dove Dale (SK 147509) near Thorpe Cloud. A smaller car park is also accessible west of the A515 at Milldale (SK 138548).

Access to the southern end of the Manifold Valley can be made from car parks on the A523 at Waterhouses (SK 085502) or at Ilam Country Park (SK 131508). For the central portion of the valley, park at either Wettonmill off the B5053 (SK 095560) or Weags Bridge (SK 100542). The northern end can be accessed from a car park at Hulme End (SK 102593) on the B5054. Most car parks are pay and display.

THE WYE VALLEY

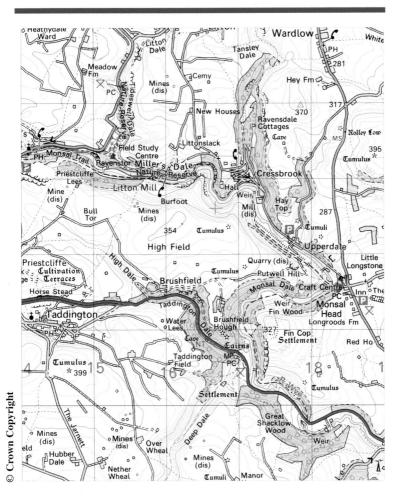

The River Wye, a major tributary of the Derwent, sustains a continuous flow of water across the entire limestone outcrop of the White Peak. Trending broadly in a north-west to south-east direction over a distance of some 50km the Wye receives numerous tributary valleys, the majority of which show the characteristic dry form deeply cut into the plateau surface. Many are worth exploring for their geomorphological interest and scenic attraction, and viewpoints such as Monsal Head (SK 185716, Photo 10) are of particular note. In the area of Buxton the short headwaters of the

Photo 10: Monsal Head: *valley meander of the Wye. Photo: Roger Dalton.*

River Wye, which are initiated on the Namurian outcrop, come together and pass on to the Dinantian. The Wye can therefore be classed as an allogenic river. The valleys of these headwaters are much disfigured by reservoirs, quarries and urban development, consequently the form of the physical landscape is not always easy to decipher. However, an accessible sequence of features which illustrates the problem of the relationship between surface landform and underground drainage, is located to the south-west of Buxton (Figure 9).

At Stanley Moor (SK 042714) the junction of the Namurian shales and Dinantian limestone is marked by a group of sink holes, two of which, both 10m deep, receive short streams from the Namurian. Inspection of the form of the ground surface suggests that these streams are tributaries of the brook which flows between Grin Low (SK 054718) and Harpur Hill (SK 067712) to the east. However, Ford (1977) reports that tracer experiments have revealed that the water which disappears into these sink holes is next seen flowing on the floor of Poole's Cavern (SK 050726) over 1km to the north-east. In this show cave there is also a range of depositional phenomena which illustrate the characteristic features of a **vadose** cave system. The water eventually reaches the surface at Wye Head Springs (SK 050731) which are clearly visible at the contact between the shales and limestone in the Pavilion Gardens in central Buxton.

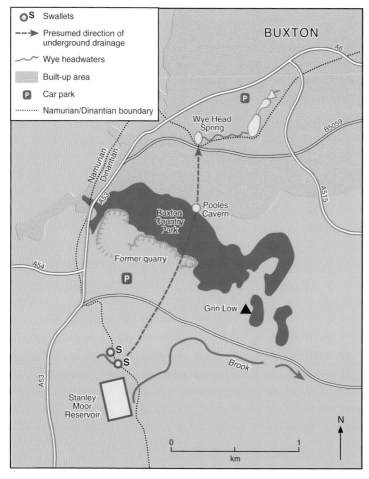

Figure 9: Drainage at Wye Head, Buxton.

To the south-east lies a major tributary of the Wye, the River Lathkill. Lathkill Dale illustrates various aspects of dry valley form as well as the relationship between surface form and sub-surface drainage (Figure 10). The upper part of Lathkill Dale is aligned west to east and broadly correlates with the trend and axis of the Lathkill Dale Syncline. Viewed from the upper flanks of the Dale a two-stage origin is suggested, the initial stage being represented by a broad, shallow depression into which the present dale is trenched. Between the access to Lathkill Dale east of Monyash at SK 157665 and Cales Dale three distinct sections can be identified.

The first, to the confluence with Fern Dale (SK 161661), has the shallow open form typical of dry valleys (Photo 11) but is modified by the presence of a low free face, 1-2m in height, on the north-facing side. Beyond Fern Dale the valley becomes gorge-like as local resistant reef limestone outcrops restrict lateral development (Figure

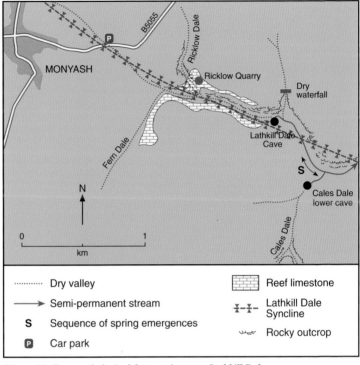

Figure 10: Geomorphological features in upper Lathkill Dale.

10). The reefs form overhanging features above weaker well-jointed limestone beds. These are often cuspate where water seepages suggest freeze-thaw activity may have been effective. Below Ricklow Quarry (SK 170660) the gradient of the valley floor steepens, the valley widens and the form of the valley sides becomes more complex with a succession of free faces and screes, the latter coalescing across the valley floor. The screes may be exposed or vegetated, in which case the turf often appears poorly bonded with the underlying scree and is, therefore, vulnerable. A third section of the valley begins at Lathkill Dale Cave (SK 171659), beyond which the depth of the valley below the plateau exceeds 50m. The greater parts of the valley sides are made up of scree which rests uniformly at angles of about 30° but with a noticeable concavity at the valley floor and above exposures of limestone. Following wet conditions the River Lathkill flows strongly from the cave and may receive seepage from the valley floor. Down valley an important tributary emerges in Cales Dale at the lower cave (SK 173653), while a series of springs break out along the valley side. However, all these features are often dry in dry weather. Although the tributary opposite Lathkill Dale Cave is permanently dry, evidence of former fluvial activity is present in the form of a spring-sapped notch in the valley floor and a 6m high dry waterfall which marks a clear-cut break in the valley profile (Photo 12).

Photo 11: Permanently dry upper section of Lathkill Dale *showing characteristic cross-profile rock outcrops and scree slopes. Photo: Roger Dalton.*

Photo 12: A dry tributary valley *on the north side of Lathkill Dale, showing former waterfall feature. Photo: Roger Dalton.*

Clearly the presence of rivers which flow intermittently is indicative of underground drainage responsive to climatic conditions. Ford (1977) reports explorations of incomplete semi-vadose systems extending from the Knotlow and Hillocks mines west of Monyash (SK 143676) to the Lathkill and Cales Dale caves which suggest an underground pattern roughly coincidental with surface form.

Access

The features in the Buxton area can be easily reached from the A53. Parking is available at Buxton Country Park and Poole's Cavern to the south of Buxton, from which it is a short walk south to inspect the swallet holes on Stanley Moor. A fee is charged at the entrance to Poole's Cavern. Wye Head Spring rises in the Pavilion Gardens in central Buxton.

Lathkill Dale deserves to be explored on foot; allow a full day for traversing and returning along the Dale. Roadside parking is available at the head of the Dale, east of Monyash village (SK 157664) on the B5055. A minor road off the B5055 leads to Over Haddon where there is a large car park (SK 203665) from which it is a short walk downhill to the Dale. Much of Lathkill Dale is a National Nature Reserve and permission is required from the warden (who works for English Nature and is based at Over Haddon; Tel: 01629 815095) to carry out fieldwork away from public rights of way.

Monsal Head car park (SK 184714) on the B6465 offers splendid views of and easy access to a classic section of the Wye Valley.

THE
DERWENT VALLEY

The valley of the River Derwent is one of the most important features of the Peak District landscape. In the north, the valley occupies a central position in the gritstone uplands of the Dark Peak, where its deep incision has been utilised to create the impressive reservoirs of Howden, Derwent and Ladybower (Figure 2, page 10). Further south the valley is more marginal, and effectively separates the Dinantian limestones of the White Peak in the west from the prominent scarps and ridges of the Namurian sandstones to the east (Figure 11b).

From its source in the peat moorlands north-east of Bleaklow Hill (SK 105964), the incipient River Derwent winds its way eastwards and then southwards accumulating waters from numerous moorland streams. In these circuitous upper reaches it is possible to trace the progressive development of a major river valley from a small gully carved in the peat. Below its confluence with the River Ashop at Ladybower (SK 193863) the Derwent becomes a much more substantial river, being further augmented by the waters of the River Noe south of Bamford and then by the River Wye at Rowsley. Between Rowsley and Matlock, the width of the valley increases significantly and the river meanders over a well established floodplain. In this section the north-west to south-east trend of the valley is broadly parallel to the regional strike of the bedrock (Figure 1), and the valley floor is developed on relatively soft Namurian shales. At Matlock, there is a marked change in valley form and direction as the river encounters the eastern extremity of the main limestone outcrop (Figure 11). From here as far as Cromford, 4km downstream, the river flows southwards through a narrow steep-sided gorge with precipitous limestone cliffs. On reaching Cromford, however, the Derwent reverts to a south-easterly route and departs from the Peak District in a narrow winding valley cut obliquely across the Namurian outcrop.

Despite its broad parallelism to the regional strike of the Carboniferous strata, the Derwent Valley is a somewhat anomalous element in the Peak District landscape. At Hathersage and Matlock Bath, for example, it cuts through a series of local folds while downstream from Cromford it transects several prominent sandstone horizons in the Namurian sequence with little regard to structure. Thus the course taken by the river is not always easy to explain and needs to be considered in the context of both the region's geomorphological evolution and its relationship to the underlying geology.

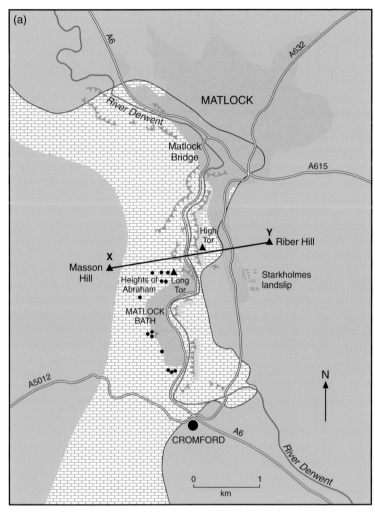

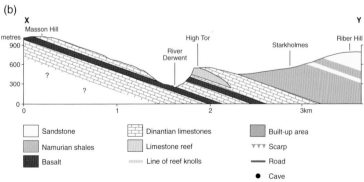

Figure 11: The Derwent Gorge at Matlock: (a) location and geological relationship, and (b) detailed cross-section.

The early stages of the drainage history of the Peak District are uncertain since traces of former valleys have been modified or obliterated by subsequent erosion. It is generally assumed that the initial drainage lines were developed on an eastward-sloping surface of Mesozoic rocks (now removed) produced as a result of uplift and tilting during the Tertiary. This view envisages that a series of eastward-flowing consequent rivers extended across the area and channelled surface waters towards the North Sea. Two such rivers are thought to have been the proto-Trent in south Derbyshire and the proto-Wye further north. Each is considered to have been fed by north-south tributaries of which the lower and middle reaches of the present River Derwent could be remnants. A similar eastward-flowing consequent river to the north of the proto-Wye has also been postulated, and would have taken tributary waters from the upper reaches of the River Derwent. If this view is correct, subsequent incision of the developing drainage lines would have resulted in their eventual superimposition on underlying Carboniferous rocks. It is necessary to envisage lateral extension and progressive unification of appropriate north-south tributaries to create the present drainage line of the River Derwent. By gradually extending its valley northwards in this way, the Derwent is thought to have captured the headwaters of former eastward-flowing consequent rivers and thus was ultimately responsible for a major change in the drainage pattern of the Peak District.

In theory, a combination of superimposition and river capture could account for many anomalies in the present-day drainage of the Peak District. Unequivocal evidence of such activity is nevertheless difficult to find. The picture is undoubtedly complicated by the impact of climatically induced fluctuations in the behaviour of geomorphological systems during the Pleistocene (Table 1, page 8) the full effect of which is still imperfectly understood. Matlock Gorge and the Pilsley Terrace serve to illustrate such complications.

Matlock Gorge

The narrow twisting gorge occupied by the River Derwent on its north-south route between Matlock and Cromford (Figure 11a) represents a spectacular example of discordance in the local drainage pattern. Here the river has cut a deep cleft through a broad anticlinal fold in the Dinantian limestones with little regard to the geological structure. The fold plunges eastwards beneath a cover of Namurian shales, and the limestones exposed in the gorge show considerable variation in both the amount and direction of their dip. One further complication is the presence, within the limestone sequence, of irregular reef knolls and basaltic lavas (Figure 11b). These have been incised by the River Derwent and now outcrop along the precipitous valley sides (Photo 13).

The Matlock Gorge is anomalous because the River Derwent could have followed a simpler route along the shale outcrop only a few hundred metres further east. Such a course would seem to be more

Photo 13: Matlock Gorge limestone outcrops. Looking north-east from the Heights of Abraham. *Photo: Derbyshire Dales District Council.*

natural, particularly if the river, on cutting down through the Namurian sequence, had migrated laterally down the dip of the shales, thus shifting the valley progressively eastwards (Figure 11b). However, **uniclinal** movement of this sort may have been obstructed by bedrock irregularities. For example, it has been suggested that the limestone reef knolls which project upwards into the shales on the east side of the Gorge could have formed a barrier to lateral migration by the river (Ford and Burek, 1976). Thus if the ancestral Derwent flowed to the west of its present position, uniclinal shift would have caused eastwards migration down-dip until the river became trapped by the line of reef knolls encountered at Matlock Bath (Figure 11b). Vertical incision must then have predominated so that the river excavated its anomalous gorge through the limestone.

The depth of downcutting into the limestones is approximately 120m when measured vertically from the top of the prominent reef knoll forming High Tor (SK 298589). Major fluctuations in climate, amongst other factors, may have been responsible for significant variations in the rate of incision by causing base level changes to which the river was obliged to respond. It is possible that incision was enhanced during cold episodes, either by the presence of glacial meltwaters or as a result of the increased seasonal discharge associated with periglacial streams. However, the existence of glacial and periglacial episodes may have had a much more profound effect on the development of the river. There is reason to suspect that the Derwent was diverted to its present position from a former course along the shale outcrop to the east of High Tor (Figure 11b). This is because, at Matlock Bridge (SK 298602), the river seems to undertake a deliberate change of direction in order to flow over the limestone. In so doing it cuts across the line of reef knolls which should have formed a barrier to it if the uniclinal shift explanation outlined above is correct. Diversion might have been caused by glaciation, although there is no independent evidence to support this view. An alternative possibility is that the river was deflected onto the limestone by a major landslip on the eastern valley side at Matlock. Mass movement of this type appears to have been a relatively common occurrence on slopes underlain by Namurian shales in the Peak District: for example, at Mam Tor and in the Edale Valley. Although occasional failures still take place, it is likely that instability was much more intense when slopes were being weakened by a range of periglacial processes or were being loaded by glacier ice. Evidence of recent landslips can be found at several localities in the Derwent Valley area, most spectacularly at Oker Hill (SK 271613) and also at Starkholmes (SK 302588). Since their surface form becomes increasingly degraded with time, older landslips may have little topographic expression today. This would certainly be the case at Matlock, where diversion of the River Derwent must have taken place well before the post-glacial period. Such an hypothesis is difficult to prove, but would gain support if the former slip planes were discovered, perhaps buried in shale bedrock beneath the solifluction deposits on Matlock Bank (SK 298605) and Matlock Cliff (SK 313597).

Pilsley Terrace

Pilsley Terrace is a distinct bench-like feature which forms an arc from Baslow through Bakewell to Rowsley in the region of the middle Derwent Valley (Figure 12). The Terrace has been interpreted by Straw (1968) as the dissected remnants of a former valley floor and he thought it represented an abandoned course of the River Derwent. It is particularly well developed south-west of Pilsley, although here it has been cut by the River Wye and now lies at a height of over 60m above the modern floodplain. The Terrace appears to reflect a period of prolonged erosion since it is developed within a narrow altitudinal range on different rock types ranging from Dinantian limestones to Namurian shales and sandstones. An identical feature can be traced up the Derwent Valley north of Baslow and also downstream to the south of Rowsley. It has not, however, been identified in the Chatsworth Park section of the Derwent Valley lying between Baslow and Rowsley. Significantly, within this section the river has cut through a resistant sandstone member in the Namurian sequence and occupies a narrower and more anomalous valley.

There is evidence that glaciation played a major part in the

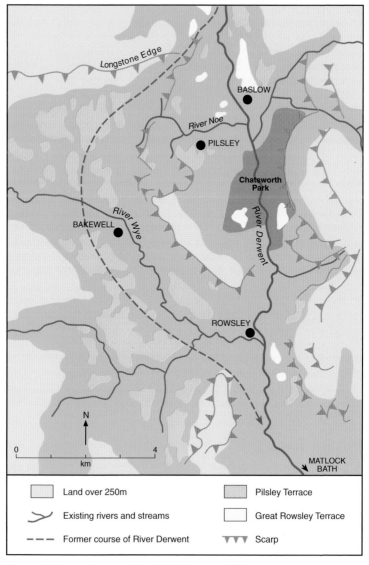

Figure 12: Terrace features of the Middle Derwent Valley.

development of the drainage pattern south of Baslow. A study of the distribution of glacial deposits within the area shows that these are preserved almost exclusively on remnants of the Pilsley Terrace. The absence of glacial deposits in the Chatsworth Park section implies that the Pilsley Terrace route was in existence prior to glaciation and that the present course of the River Derwent through Chatsworth Park is a later development. One possible explanation is that during deglaciation, the former Pilsley Terrace route was obstructed, either by a stagnant ice body or by thick deposits of till. Consequently glacial meltwaters excavated a new valley between Baslow and Rowsley which was subsequently adopted by the River Derwent (Figure 11). It is notable that a lower terrace, the Great Rowsley Terrace standing at 3m above the modern floodplain in Chatsworth Park, extends along the Derwent Valley and is considered to be the product of the river immediately following glaciation (Figure 12).

Access

Most of the Derwent Valley is accessible by road. From the south the A6 can be followed northwards through Matlock to Rowsley and then the B6012 via Chatsworth Park to Baslow. From here the A623 and B6001 can be taken to Hathersage after which the A625 and A6013 are followed to Ladybower Reservoir. From the north the reverse journey can be made from the A57. North of the Ladybower and Derwent reservoirs, access to the Derwent Valley is difficult and must be made on foot.

The Pilsley Terrace can be viewed from the road by taking the A6 from Rowsley to Bakewell, then turning onto the A619 to Baslow and either staying on this road or turning north-west onto the B6001 to Calver. On a clear day a good vantage point from which to ponder over the possibility of glacial diversion is at SK 257729 on the footpath above Baslow village or from Baslow Edge itself. From here the eye can follow a route south-south-westwards across the Pilsley Terrace to the River Wye or southwards along the line of the Hathersage Terrace to Chatsworth Park and Rowsley.

The best points from which to see the overall characteristics of the Derwent Valley are high up on the valley sides or on adjacent hills. A good view of the anomalous Matlock Gorge can be obtained by looking northwards from the summit of Bolehill (SK 294554), 1km south of Cromford. Cars may be parked at the Black Rocks picnic site (SK 291556). This vantage point also offers an extensive panorama taking in the limestone plateau to the west, together with the gritstone moorlands to the east where the discordant route of the River Derwent below Cromford may be clearly seen. An alternative view of the Gorge is obtained by looking southwards from the high ground of Matlock Bath near the County Offices in Matlock (SK 300606). Spectacular views within the limestone gorge itself are available from the summit of High Tor (SK 297589) or Prospect Tower on the Heights of Abraham (SK 293586) in Matlock Bath. Both need to be approached on foot from car parks in Matlock or Matlock Bath. The Heights of Abraham can also be reached by cable-car from the station car park. Entry fees are charged.

THE NORTHERN FRINGE

Rushup Vale, Winnats Pass and Hope Valley

The northern fringe of the White Peak is an area of striking relief and character. This reflects the juxtaposition of two contrasting sequences of rocks which have responded differently to denudation. The Dinantian limestones give rise to landscapes developed largely by processes of solution, whereas the Namurian shales and sandstones provide a varied range of process-response conditions in producing more upstanding relief. Two west to east trending valleys, Rushup Vale and Hope Valley, are separated by a short watershed of limestone running south-west from Mam Tor (Figure 13). Both valleys have pronounced northern sides developed in Namurian rocks and southern sides cut in limestone. In Hope Valley the limestone forms a distinct escarpment broken by a number of short, deeply incised dry valleys

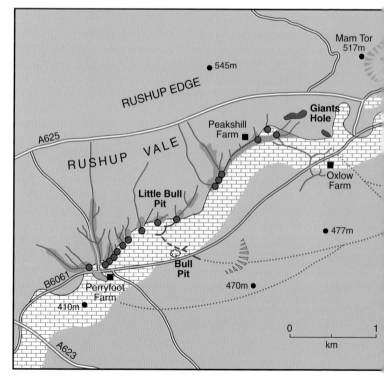

Figure 13: Features of the northern limestone margin.

44

but in Rushup Vale the slopes are more subdued. Whilst surface topography would suggest the drainage of the two valleys is quite separate, sub-surface flow beneath the watershed actually forms a direct link between them (Figure 14). A number of interesting geomorphological features associated with these unusual drainage conditions are visible in both valleys.

The limestone-shale junction running through Rushup Vale has a variety of associated solution features and swallets. Bull Pit (SK 106814) on the southern valley side (Figure 13) is a large doline up to 50m in diameter and nearly 50m deep with sheer walls. It probably represents a collapse structure produced by the sub-surface solution of limestone beneath a former shale cover. In contrast, swallets found along the valley bottom would seem to have been formed by the action of surface streams. The smooth, low-angled, lower slopes of Rushup Edge and the valley bottom are developed upon a solifluction deposit (head) up to 6m thick. These deposits are composed largely of sandstone and shale debris and are thought to date from the late Devensian. Their emplacement covered the shale-limestone junction and obliterated former drainage lines. Subsequently the periglacial waste was gullied by streams flowing down from Rushup Edge. On encountering the underlying limestone these streams were diverted underground in a series of swallets. In some cases the water enters the

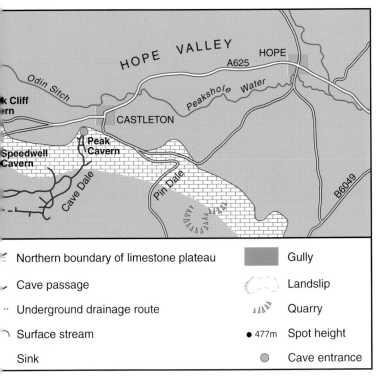

Northern boundary of limestone plateau		Gully
Cave passage		Landslip
Underground drainage route		Quarry
Surface stream	● 477m	Spot height
Sink	◯	Cave entrance

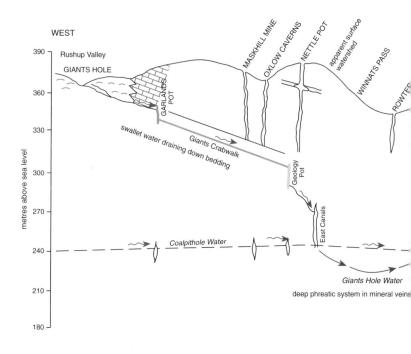

Figure 14: The Castleton cave systems – west to east. After: Ford, 1996.

limestone laterally at the end of an elongated depression up to 10m deep. Little Bull Pit (SK 104817 and see Figure 13) provides a good example of an active swallet with a stream entering a cave 3m in height at the foot of a small limestone cliff. In some of the depressions the original swallets have been abandoned as more of the limestone has been revealed by continued stream downcutting. The largest of the swallets, Giant's Hole (SK 119827), also forms the highest of the series with its entrance at an elevation of 373m.

The drainage of the swallets together with percolation water from several square kilometres of limestone has given rise to the most extensive system of caves in the Peak District (Figures 13 and 14). Cave research and dye tests have shown that the water passes along mineral veins and tube-like passages produced by phreatic zone solution. The water emerges in a resurgence at Russet Well in Peak Cavern gorge (Figure 14) having passed beneath the surface watershed between Rushup Vale and Hope Valley and moved down through 150m of limestone. The course of the subterranean drainage also passes through the inner parts of Speedwell Cavern and beneath the stream draining Peak Cavern. The other large caves, Blue John and Treak Cliff caverns, are apparently unrelated to this sub-surface flow route. These latter caves are thought to have been produced in

EAST

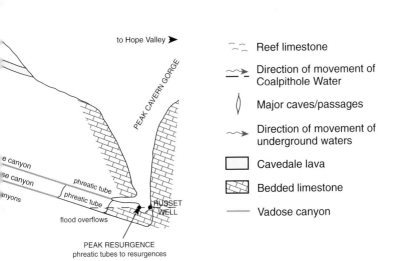

to Hope Valley ➤

PEAK CAVERN GORGE

e canyon
se canyon
anyons

phreatic tube
phreatic tube

flood overflows

RUSSET
WELL

PEAK RESURGENCE
phreatic tubes to resurgences

Reef limestone

Direction of movement of
Coalpithole Water

Major caves/passages

Direction of movement of
underground waters

Cavedale lava

Bedded limestone

Vadose canyon

part by waters derived from Windy Knoll (SK 125829) and high-level sink holes at the eastern end of Rushup Vale.

Speedwell, Peak, Blue John and Treak Cliff caverns are renowned features of the Castleton area. They are all open to the public and provide an opportunity to examine many of the geomorphological features of cave systems. Phreatic tube passages which have been further incised by vadose flow conditions are a characteristic feature. Good examples of stalagmites, stalactites, **flowstone** and a variety of cave sediments are also to be seen. The dating of stalagmites by uranium/thorium isotope methods in conjunction with the analysis of cave sediments has provided a tentative chronology for cave evolution. From this work (see Ford, 1977; 1996) it would appear a substantial amount of cave development took place prior to the late Pleistocene (Table 1, page 8).

The limestone escarpment of the southern side of the Hope Valley is dissected by three large dry valleys, Pin Dale, Cave Dale and Winnats Pass (Figure 13). The most famous, and most dramatic, is the deep gorge formed by the Winnats Pass (which is a National Trust property) (Photo 14). This dry valley is 1km in length with an overall gradient of approximately 9°. It is 150m deep with a narrow, twisting floor enclosed by precipitous bluffs of limestone. Small caves occur

Photo 14: The gorge-like character of the exhumed reef channel of Winnats Pass.
Photo: Frances Dalton.

in the valley sides. There is geological evidence to suggest that the present-day valley follows the route of a mid-Carboniferous inter-reef channel which was filled with eroded reef material and, later, Namurian shales. Part of this evidence, the Beach Beds, comprising a distinctive assemblage of well-rounded shell debris, is to be found in a quarry at SK 138827. Pin Dale and Cave Dale could conceivably have similar developmental histories.

Several hypotheses have been put forward to explain the subsequent re-excavation of the channel and the formation of the gorge. Cavern collapse, once suggested as the origin of Winnats Pass, may be discounted because there is no supporting evidence. A more acceptable explanation is that surface streams tributary to Peakshole Water (itself a tributary of the River Noe) cut the valley when water levels in the limestone were higher. Progressive desiccation of Winnats Pass and the other dales then took place as Peakshole Water incised more rapidly into the shales of Hope Valley. Irregularities in the long profile of Winnats Pass, Pin Dale and Cave Dale may be accounted for by this process, although these dry valleys may simply represent gradient adjustments by former surface streams due to bedrock constraints on channel width. One widely held view is that much of the excavation of the gorge was produced by surface flow across frozen, and hence impermeable, limestone during cold phases of the Pleistocene. In fact the age of initial cutting of Winnats Pass remains uncertain, but cave studies indicate that incision must post-date the creation of high-level phreatic fissures. This phreatic solution has been dated to the early Pleistocene. Ford (1985) has speculated that much of the erosion of the gorge occurred as late as the Devensian cold phase. As indicated previously, dry valleys such as Winnats Pass are often multiprocess forms with a complex history. Even so, it is important to remember, at least in the case of Winnats Pass, that events in the mid-Carboniferous, some 300 million years BP, may have contributed significantly to the present-day form of the valley.

Access

The swallets of Rushup Vale all lie on private farmland. Enquiries for access to those at the western end of the series can be made at Perryfoot Farm (SK 101812) and to Giant's Hole from Peakshill Farm (SK 115826). Access fees may be charged. A footpath crosses the valley from the A625 to to B6061, passing close to Bull Pit and Little Bull Pit (SK 107814). Roadside parking is difficult and the nearest car park is situated by the A625 south-west of Mam Tor. Parking fees may be charged.

The A625 road west of Castleton by Mam Tor is permanently closed by landslips. Access to Rushup Vale from the Castleton direction is via Winnats Pass but the road is suitable for cars and minibuses only. A car park exists at the eastern end of Winnats Pass at SK 140829. Parking in the Pass is prohibited.

The Speedwell, Peak, Blue John and Treak Cliff caverns are open to the public for most of the year and have car parks. Entrance fees are charged.

GLOSSARY

Allogenic. Originating from outside the immediate environment.

Anticline. A rock sequence which has been upfolded.

BP. Years before present.

Carbonate platform. A sub-marine shelf area where limestone deposits are built upwards.

Clast. A fragment of rock.

Dolomite. A rock type in which calcium carbonate has been replaced by magnesium carbonate.

Dry valley. A streamless valley once apparently occupied by a perennial stream.

Exhumed. Referring to landscape features once buried but now revealed by erosion.

Flowstone. Carbonate deposits precipitated from supersaturated water flowing through limestones.

Free face. A near vertical rock exposure.

Head. An accumulation of poorly sorted debris formed under freeze/thaw conditions in a periglacial environment.

Inlier. A rock outcrop surrounded by rocks of younger age.

Interstitial. The spaces between clasts.

Loess. A deposit of fine, silty, wind blown particles derived from vegetation-free surfaces during the Quaternary.

Mass movement. The movement of weathered material downslope *en masse*.

Peneplanation. A process resulting in the creation of a planation surface.

Periglacial. Term describing a cold climate environment characteristic of the margins of ice sheets and glaciers.

Permafrost. Permanently frozen ground only thawing at the surface in the summer season.

Phreatic. Of the zone in a permeable rock which is saturated.

Planation surface. A nearly level land surface planed across geological structures.

Sink (swallet). The passage in permeable rock through which a surface stream disappears underground.

Slip planes. Inclined surfaces such as bedding planes or joints along which blocks or masses of rock have moved, i.e. slipped under gravity.

Solifluction. Downslope movement of surface material frequently activated by alternate freezing and thawing under periglacial conditions.

Speleothem. Carbonate deposits in the form of stalactites/stalagmites.

Superimposed. Of a drainage pattern developed conformably with one geological structure, then lowered by erosion onto an underlying structure.

Swallet. See sink.

Syncline. A rock sequence which has been downfolded.

Till. The ill-sorted debris deposited by an ice sheet or glacier.

Tor. A feature of a hill slope or hilltop made up of conspicuous upstanding rock outcrops.

Tuff. Consolidated volcanic ash.

Uniclinal. Where a stream has been guided by the inclination of the strata to move laterally down-dip as downcutting has proceeded. The resultant valley form is asymmetrical.

Vadose. Of the non-saturated zone within a permeable rock through which water percolates via joints and bedding planes.

BIBLIOGRAPHY

Aitkenhead, N., Chisholm, J.I. and Stevenson, J.P. (1985) 'Geology of the country around Buxton, Leek and Bakewell', *Memoirs of the British Geological Survey*, Sheet 111. London: HMSO.

Burek, C.V. (1991) 'Quaternary history and glacial deposits of the Peak District' in Ehlers, J., Gibbard, P.L. and Rose, J. (eds) *Glacial Deposits in Britain and Ireland*. Rotterdam: Balkema, pp. 193-201.

Dalton, R., Fox, H. and Jones, P. (1999) *Classic Landforms of the Dark Peak*. Sheffield: Geographical Association.

Doornkamp, J.C. (1990) 'Landslides of Derbyshire', *East Midland Geographer*, 13, pp. 33-62.

Ford, T.D. (ed) (1977) *Limestone and Caves of the Peak District*. Norwich: Geobooks.

Ford, T.D. (1985) 'The Castleton caves: results of speleothem dating' in Briggs, D.J., Gilbertson, D.D. and Jenkinson, R.D.S. (eds) *Peak District and Northern Dukeries Field Guide*. Cambridge: Quaternary Research Association, pp. 81-7.

Ford, T.D. (1987) 'The origin of the Winnats Pass, Derbyshire', *Mercian Geologist*, 10, pp. 241-249.

Ford, T.D. (1996) 'Speleogenesis: the evolution of the Castleton caves', *Geology Today*, 12, pp. 101-109.

Ford, T.D. and Burek, C.V. (1976) 'Anomalous limestone gorges in Derbyshire', *Mercian Geologist*, 6, pp. 59-66.

Goudie, A. (1990) *The Landforms of England and Wales*, Chapter 7 – Karst. Oxford: Blackwell, pp. 215-242.

Gunn, J. (1985) 'Pennine karst areas and their Quaternary history' in Johnson, R.H. (ed) *The Geomorphology of North West England*. Manchester: Manchester University Press, pp. 263-281.

Johnson, R.H. (1967) 'Some glacial, periglacial and karstic landforms in the Sparrowpit-Dove Holes area of North Derbyshire', *East Midland Geographer*, 4, pp. 224-238.

Pitty, A. (1968) 'The scale and significance of solution loss from the limestone tract of the Pennines', *Proceedings of the Geologists Association*, 79, pp. 153-177.

Stevenson, I.P. and Gaunt, G.D. (1971) 'Geology of the country around Chapel-en-le-Frith', *Memoirs of the British Geological Survey*, Sheet 99. London: HMSO.

Straw, A. (1968) 'A Pleistocene diversion of drainage in North Derbyshire', *East Midland Geographer*, 4, pp. 275-280.

Sweeting, M.M. (1972) *Karst Landforms*. London: Macmillan.

Walsh, P.T., Boulter, M.C., Ijtabo, A. and Urbani, D.M. (1972) 'The preservation of the Neogene Brassington Formation of the southern Pennines and its bearing on the evolution of upland Britain', *Journal of the Geological Society of London*, 128, pp. 519-559.

Warwick, G.T. (1964) 'Dry valleys of the southern Pennines, England', *Erdkunde*, 18, pp. 116-123.